Minibeasts

by Anne Giulieri
illustrated by Gaston Vanzet

Look down here.

Here comes
a little worm.

The little worm
is down the hole.

The hole is little.

Look up here.

Here comes
a little caterpillar.

The little caterpillar
is on the leaf.

The leaf is little.

Look down here.

Here comes
a little ant.

The little ant
is in the nest.

The nest is big.

Look up here.

Here comes
a little spider.

The little spider
is on the web.

The web is big.

16